Progress with Oxford

Shape and Size

Hello, I'm Max, and this is Min!

Contents

Key

 Count

 Write

 Trace with pencil

 Match

 Circle

 Colour

 Draw

 Play together

 Find the sticker

 Trace with finger

 Say it

OXFORD
UNIVERSITY PRESS

Naming shapes

Can you trace these shapes with your finger?

Say the names.

What is your favourite shape?

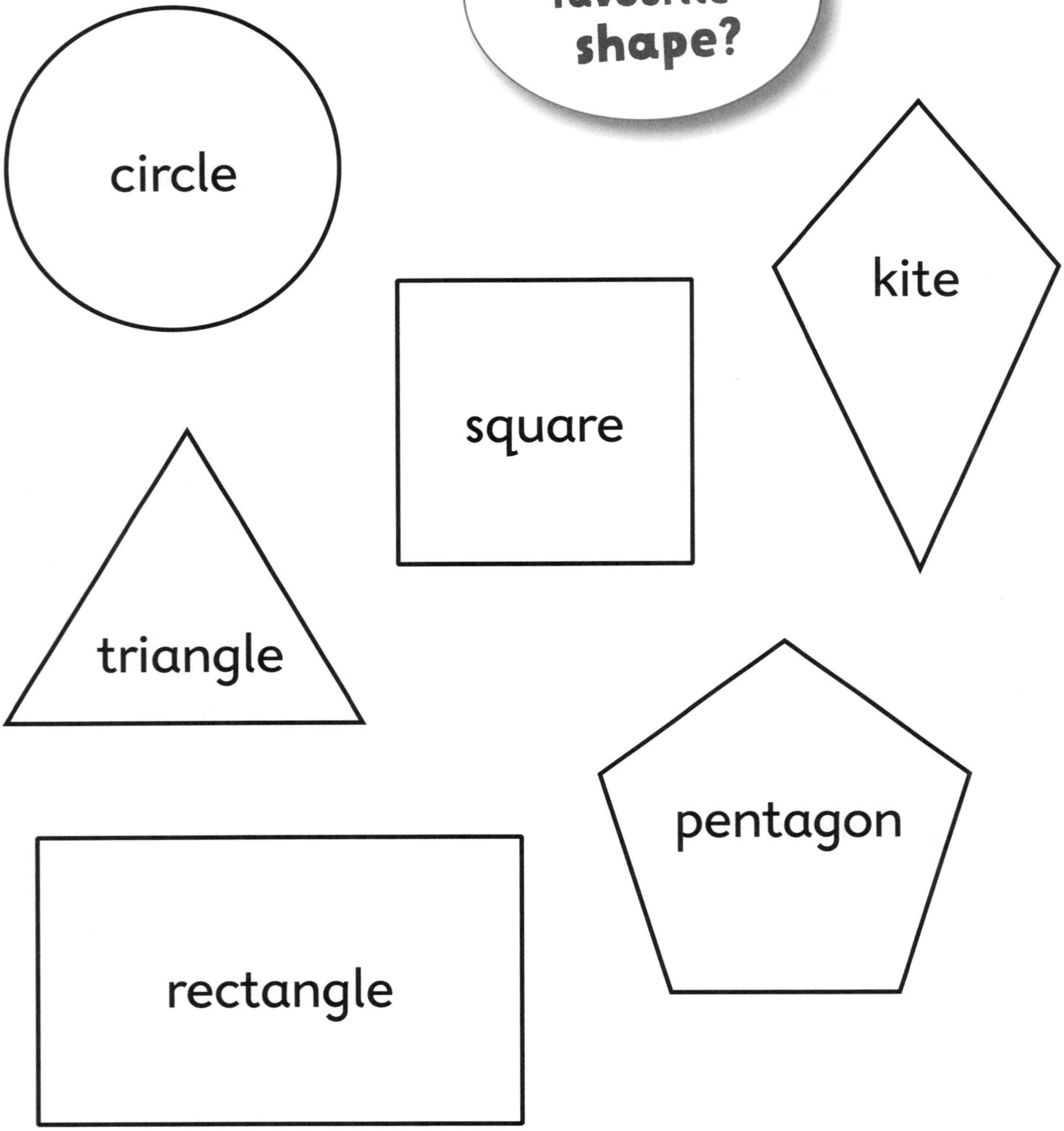

circle

kite

square

triangle

pentagon

rectangle

Colour the triangles red.

Colour the squares blue.

Colour the circles yellow.

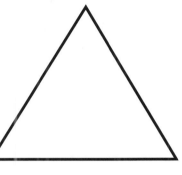

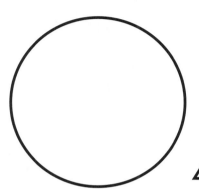

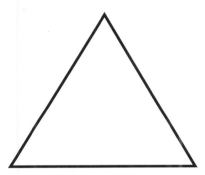

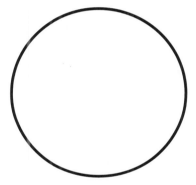

Find and name shapes all around you.

 Play with shapes.

Go for a walk in the park. Look at the shapes of different leaves.

Ask a grown-up to draw you a shape. Name the shape they draw.

Look at the shape of bricks in a brick wall and paving stones on a pavement.

Give yourself a sticker

Now – track how you're doing on page 32!

Shape match

 Match the shape to the object of the same shape.

Do you know the names of the shapes?

Go on a **shape hunt** around your house!

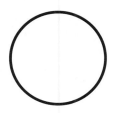 **Circle the object that matches the shape.**

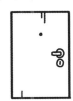  

   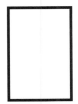

Yum! I love triangle shapes like pizza and cake!

Give yourself a sticker

Drawing shapes

Trace over the shapes.

Can you remember the names of the shapes?

Copy the shapes.

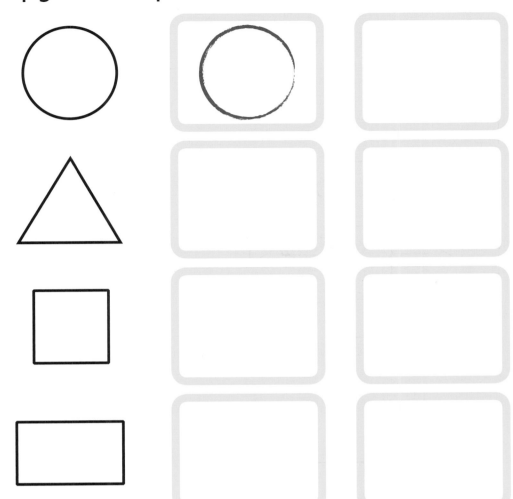

Have more fun making shapes.

 ## Play with shapes.

Fill a closable sandwich bag with hair gel and glitter. Close it and flatten it. Draw shapes on the bag.

Draw shapes on the pavement with water and a paintbrush.

Draw shapes on your friend's back. Can they guess the shape?

Well done!

Give yourself a sticker

Rockets and robots

 Complete the robot.

 Complete the rocket.

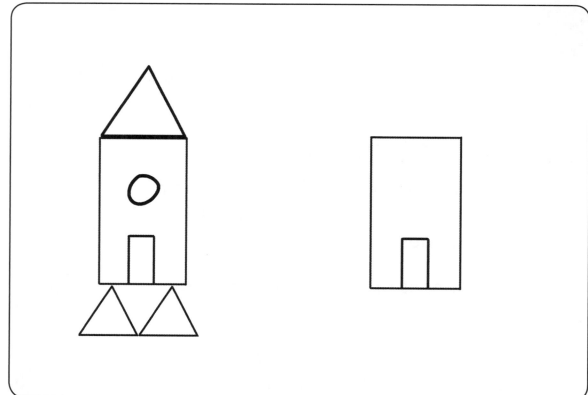

Flowers

 Add shape stickers to these circles to make flowers.

Look at us! We look like a rocket!

Give yourself a sticker

 Play with shapes.

Use bricks or empty boxes and pots to build models. Tell a friend what shapes you have used.

Now – track how you're doing on page 32!

Sides and corners

This square has 4 sides.

4

This square has 4 corners.

4

A shape has sides and corners.

Count the sides.

Count the corners.

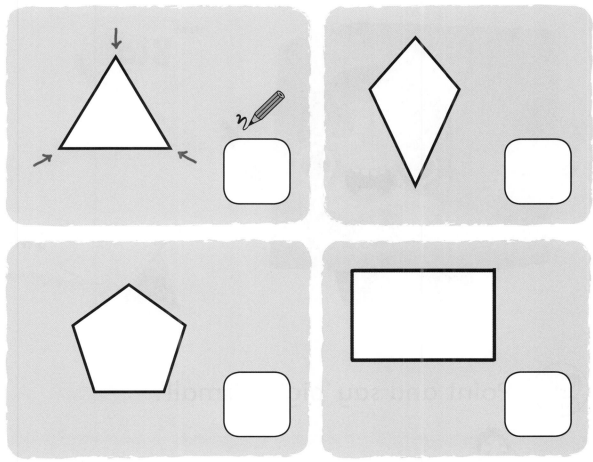

 Can you find more shapes and count their corners?

Well done!

 Play with shapes.

Point and say the name of each shape on this page: triangle, square, rectangle, kite, pentagon.

Find shapes at home. Count the sides. Count the corners.

Count the corners on a box.

Give yourself a sticker

Big and small

 Point and say 'big' or 'small'.

Circle the **biggest** in each pair.

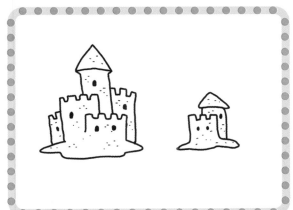

Compare the sizes of the different pairs of shoes in your home.

Give yourself a sticker

13

Now – track how you're doing on page 32!

Same and different

 Cross out the one that is a **different** size.

I always have the bigger cake!

Draw a line to match the socks that are the **same** size.

 Trace the shape that is the **same** size.

Now – track how you're doing on page 32!

Big, bigger, biggest

Time for presents!

big   bigger   biggest

 Say the words big, bigger, biggest.

 Put the stickers in the right order.

Big   Bigger   Biggest

Stickers for page 9

Stickers for page 16

Stickers for page 18

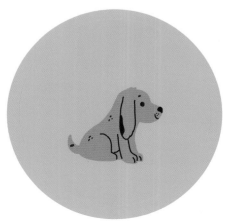

Reward Stickers

Character stickers

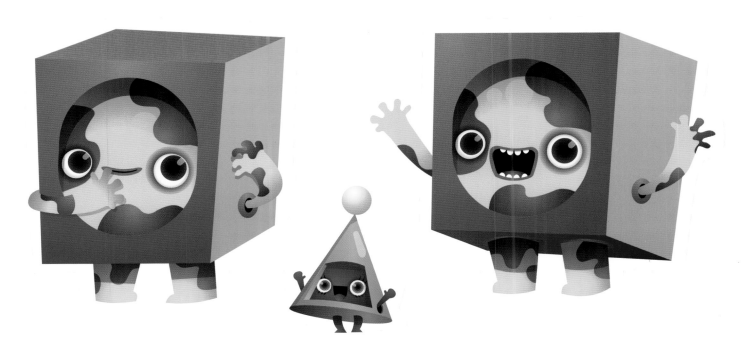

 **Circle the biggest.**

 **Tell me the story of 'Goldilocks and the Three Bears'.**

 Give yourself a sticker

Now – track how you're doing on page 32!

Small, smaller, smallest

small   smaller   smallest

 Say the words small, smaller, smallest.

 Put the stickers on the right dogs.

18

Circle the smallest.

Which ice cream do you want?

Give yourself a sticker

Now – track how you're doing on page 32!

More or less or fewer?

more   fewer

Do you like biscuits?

 Circle the picture with **more** items.

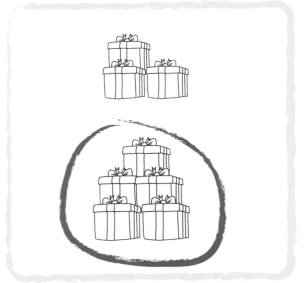

more   less

 Circle the jug that has **more**.

More or less?
More or fewer?
You decide!

 Play with sizes.

Make two piles of beads. Which has the most beads? Which has fewer?

Have a tea party with your toys. Use water for tea. Practise saying, 'Would you like some more?'

Make a jug of coloured squash. Pour it into different glasses. Which has more? Which has less?

Give
yourself
a sticker

21

Now – track how you're doing on page 32!

Full and empty

 Circle the **full** bucket in each row.

 Circle the **empty** glass in each row.

 Circle the **full** bottle in each pair.

My tummy is empty. I need my lunch!

Circle the matching container.

Go outside and play with jugs and cups of water.

Give yourself a sticker

Now – track how you're doing on page 32!

Thick, thin, wide and narrow

Ask a grown-up to read these words.

| wide | narrow | thick | thin |

 Circle the **thickest**.

Circle the **widest**.

 Have fun comparing sizes.

 Play with sizes.

Compare different lengths of spaghetti and different shapes of pasta.

Compare pieces of string and different thicknesses of wool.

Compare the sizes of different toy bricks.

Give yourself a sticker

25

Now – track how you're doing on page 32!

Longer and shorter

Which is **longer?**

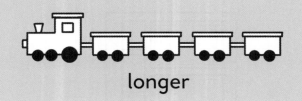 longer

 shorter

 Colour in the **longer** item.

 Colour the **shorter** item.

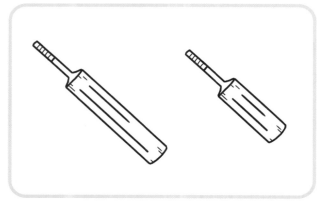

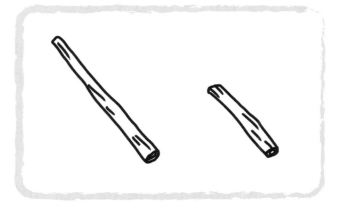

Trace over the **longer** path.

 Trace over the **longer** path.

Give yourself a sticker

Now – track how you're doing on page 32!

How far?

 ⭐⭐ Circle the **furthest**.

Who has thrown the ball the furthest?

Who has sailed the furthest?

 Trace the **shortest** path for Little Red Riding Hood.

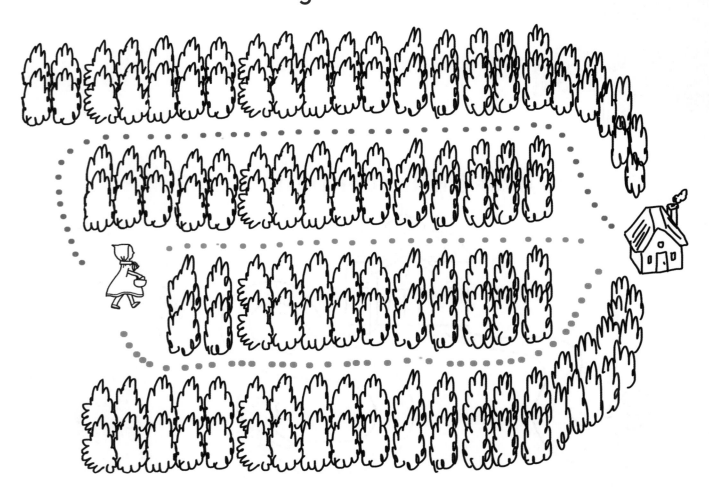

a Who walks furthest to school?

How do you get to school?

Can you work out which is further?

Play with distances.

Throw a ball with a friend. Who can throw it furthest?

....

Which is further: your school or the park?

....

Which is further: your school or where you went on holiday? Did it take a long time to travel to your holiday?

Give yourself a sticker

Now – track how you're doing on page 32!

Where is it?

Ask a grown-up to read these words.

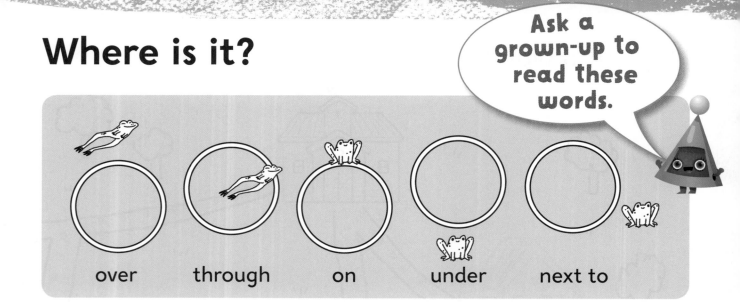

over   through   on   under   next to

 Point and say where Toby's hat is.

 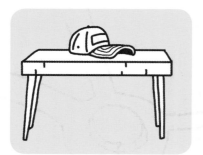 

 Where is Toby going?

Well done!

Give yourself a sticker

30   Now – track how you're doing on page 32!

Remember these?

You did it!

 Point to the item. Say the word.

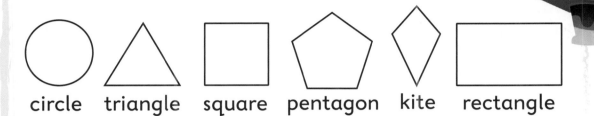

circle   triangle   square   pentagon   kite   rectangle

big   bigger   biggest

small   smaller   smallest

thick

thin

long

short

full   empty

more   less

over

under   on

next to   through

Give yourself a sticker

Now – track how you're doing on page 32!

Progress Chart

Colour in a face.

Page	I Can . . .	How did you do?		
2 – 3	I can name shapes.	😊	😐	😦
4 – 5	I can spot shapes in the world around me.	😊	😐	😦
6 – 7	I can draw shapes.	😊	😐	😦
8 – 9	I can use shapes to make patterns.	😊	😐	😦
10 – 11	I can find the corners and sides on a shape.	😊	😐	😦
12 – 13	I can use the words 'big' and 'small'.	😊	😐	😦
14 – 15	I can find two things that are the same size.	😊	😐	😦
16 – 17	I can use the words 'big', 'bigger' and 'biggest'.	😊	😐	😦
18 – 19	I can use the words 'small', 'smaller' and 'smallest'.	😊	😐	😦
20 – 21	I can use the words 'more' and 'less'.	😊	😐	😦
22 – 23	I can use the words 'full' and 'empty'.	😊	😐	😦
24 – 25	I can use the words 'thick', 'thin', 'wide' and 'narrow'.	😊	😐	😦
26 – 27	I can say when something is 'longer' or 'shorter'.	😊	😐	😦
28 – 29	I can talk about how far away something is.	😊	😐	😦
30	I can use the words 'on', 'under', 'next to', 'through' and 'over'.	😊	😐	😦
31	I can say the shape and size words.	😊	😐	😦

How did YOU do?